G000036818

Maths Everywhere

Book 1

Photocopy Masters

Tony Cotton

Collins
Educational
An imprint of HarperCollins*Publishers*

Published in 1994 by CollinsEducational
An imprint of HarperCollins*Publishers*
77-85 Fulham Palace Road
Hammersmith
London W6 8JB

This book is published in association with the Channel 4
Schools series *Maths Everywhere*. *Maths Everywhere* is
produced by Chapman Clarke Films Ltd. for Channel 4
Schools and first broadcast in the autumn term 1994.

ISBN 000 312 6412

Designed by Glynis Edwards

Illustrated by Juliet Breeze, Jerry Collins and Paul Stone

Printed by Martins the Printers, Berwick Upon Tweed

Contents

Introduction

The aim of the book

The activities in *Maths Everywhere* have been devised specifically to encourage children to use and apply maths in real life situations. In this way they begin to see themselves as everyday mathematicians and become more confident in their own mathematical ability. Introducing mathematical skills in contexts which have real relevance to children is a particularly effective way of learning and teaching maths.

The characters

The activities follow Madge the Mathemagician as she travels around in her spaceship on her quest to explore maths on Earth. She is accompanied on her journey by Tanya and Robbie, her two Earthling helpers, and Barker, her Galacta-cat.

You can introduce the characters to the children and fill them in on some of the background details by following the *Meet the crew* activity on pp. 8-9.

The content

This book is divided into five sections: *Shapes of Buildings, Patterns in Buildings, Inside Shops, Living Indoors* and *Patterns in the Home.* Each of these sections corresponds to a programme in the Channel 4 Schools *Maths Everywhere* television series and the activities can be used in conjunction with this or independently if you are not following the series.

Within each section there are six photocopiable worksheets with accompanying Teacher's notes. The worksheets are arranged progressively in order of difficulty, with two relatively easy sheets to start with (A/B), then two slightly more difficult ones (C/D) and finally two to challenge your pupils (E/F).

The level of the activity and the section/programme number appear as a corner flash on each of the children's and teacher's pages.

Section/Programme number

Shapes of Buildings

1A

Level of activity

Section/Programme title

At the end of each section there is a *Wordsheet* which lists some of the words the children have encountered in the worksheets. This *Wordsheet* takes the form of a mathematical dictionary which Madge needs to take back with her to her planet. It also provides an opportunity for children to reflect on what they have learnt and for you to assess their understanding of mathematical terms.

At the back of the book there is a section of *General sheets*. This contains resource sheets that are referenced in some of the activities e.g. squared paper, nets of cubes etc. A *What if...?* sheet (an optional extension activity) a *Pupil record sheet* (for you to record individual or class progress) are also included in this section.

Finally, a *Mathematical coverage chart* at the end of this Introduction will help you to see which areas of the maths curriculum have been covered and to plan your work accordingly.

How to use the book

The activities in this book can be used flexibly. They could form part of a whole class project, they could be used with groups of children, or individuals could work on them on their own with minimal teacher input. The teacher's notes which appear opposite each worksheet provide additional guidance. Every page of teacher's notes follows the same pattern (outlined below).

Mathematical content

This lists the mathematical concepts that children will encounter on the worksheets. This section can be used as an assessment tool, for record keeping or as a guide to future planning.

What you need

This lists any specialist equipment you may need for the activity. This section has been kept to a minimum and no unusual items are required for the activities. It also refers to any *General sheets* that you might need for the activity itself or for extension work. All the *General sheets* are grouped together at the back of the book.

How to use the sheet

These are suggestions on how to introduce the activity and what to be aware of once the children are fully involved. Again there is a minimum of instruction for those using the worksheets as stand alone activities. Ideas for follow up work and extension activities appear in the next section for those who are interested in taking the activity a step further.

Extending the activity

This section suggests ways of developing the activity more fully for teachers who want something more challenging for the whole class, for groups of children or for individuals.

What if...?

Every teacher's notes page has a *What if...?* question to extend and develop those children who show an interest or aptitude in a particular area of maths. This is an open, more challenging question which will develop children's lateral thinking as well as develop their mathematical skills. There is a blank *What if...?* sheet at the back of the book which you can use to pose these questions. Simply photocopy the blank sheet, copy on to it the relevant *What if...?* activity text and then make further copies if you want more than one child to attempt it.

Answers

A reduced copy of the children's page is shown with the answers filled in where appropriate. If the answers required are dependent on individual responses then just one example of the type of answer to expect has been provided.

Mathematical coverage

	Using and Applying Mathematics			Number and Algebra			Shape, Space and Measures				Handling Data	
	Application of mathematics	Communicating mathematics	Reasoning and logic	Knowledge and use of numbers	Estimation and approximation	Patterns and relationships	Shape	Location	Movement	Measures	Collecting data	Representing data
Shapes of Buildings												
Shapes and maps			●							●		
Sort the buildings											●	●
Wall patterns		●				●	●	●	●			
Skyscrapers		●					●					
Nets of cubes			●			●	●		●			
Building walls	●		●	●	●				●			
Patterns in Buildings												
Roof triangles		●					●					
Making pyramids	●	●					●		●	●		
Trellis walk			●			●		●	●			
Numbers in triangles			●	●	●	●						
Triangle perimeters			●	●			●			●		
Square numbers			●	●	●	●						
Inside Shops												
Sorting shopping		●	●	●							●	
Design a supermarket	●	●	●	●				●			●	
Weighing apples	●		●	●						●		
Stacking apples			●	●		●						
Stacking oranges			●	●		●						
Best bugs	●			●	●	●				●		
Living Indoors												
Delivering milk				●	●	●						
Number 7		●	●	●	●	●				●		
Pizzas		●	●	●		●						●
Stairs				●	●							
Pizza fractions	●	●		●			●					
Keeping pets	●		●	●	●							
Patterns in the Home												
Symmetry in the home	●								●			
Collecting patterns	●	●				●	●				●	●
Rangoli patterns	●	●				●	●	●	●	●		
Rod spiral			●	●	●	●	●	●	●	●		
Yoruba patterns		●							●	●		
Snowflakes	●		●	●		●	●					

7

The storyline

This book and the TV series follow Madge the Mathemagician and her crew Tanya, Robbie and Barker as they explore *Maths Everywhere* on Earth. They orbit Earth in a computerised transporter investigating different aspects of everyday life that capture their interest.

The characters

Madge's task is to compile a report to take back to her planet Mathematica. She perceives everything in purely mathematical terms but does not understand the nature of everyday life on Earth. This is where Tanya and Robbie fit in.

Robbie is inquisitive by nature and is always asking *What if...?* style questions. He is younger and less mathematically mature than Tanya but he does have flashes of inspiration.

Tanya is more pragmatic than Robbie and likes to be systematic in her approach. When faced with a mathematical challenge she is good at breaking the problem down and then suggesting the appropriate mathematical approach.

Barker, Madge's mischievous Galacta-cat, likes to get away with doing as little as possible. He is the butt of the rest of the crew's jokes but he is quick-witted and gives as good as he gets. His main interest in life is food but he has absorbed some mathematical knowledge along the way.

How to use the sheet

The aim of this sheet is to set the context for the worksheets which follow. You may like to spend some time discussing the characters and their mission so that children will feel familiar with the story as it develops.

You could also talk about the different ways that children in the class (or even teachers) approach their mathematics. Ask the children to draw themselves using the outline provided and then fill in the 3 speech bubbles.

> Hello Earthlings.
> My name is Madge and I am visiting Earth to make a report on the maths you use in your daily lives.

> Hi. My name is Tanya. I try to help Madge understand the maths here on Earth by showing her how to organise her work sensibly.

> Nice to meet you. I'm Robbie and I enjoy helping Madge but everything I see makes me ask questions.

> Hello. I am Madge's Galacta-cat. I like to do as little as possible, except when it comes to eating food!

What if Madge and her crew arrived at your home to make a report on the maths they find on Earth? In the speech bubbles write 3 things you do out of school which are mathematical.

9

Name .... Date ....

Shapes of Buildings

Setting the scene

Madge and her fellow travellers look down on Earth from their spaceship. Madge recognises the buildings they see as 3-D shapes which look 2-D when viewed from above. This interest in buildings leads our intrepid explorers to look at the number of bricks needed to build a wall and the patterns that can be made out of bricks.

The worksheets in this section are:

1A Shapes and maps
recognising 2-D shapes

1B Sort the buildings
recognising 3-D shapes

1C Wall patterns
describing patterns

1D Skyscrapers
views and plans

1E Nets of cubes
nets and symmetry

1F Building walls
multiplication and factors

Shapes of Buildings Wordsheet
mathematical language

Shapes and maps

Mathematical content

The children will be asked to:

- ❐ recognise and name common 2-D shapes
- ❐ choose appropriate mathematical equipment
- ❐ use realistic measurements and/or scales
- ❐ use the language of shape and space to describe shapes

What you need

- ❐ coloured pencils or crayons (red, blue, green and yellow)
- ❐ map or plan of your local area (for *Extending the activity*)

How to use the sheet

Talk about the sorts of shapes you might see if you viewed the Earth from a spaceship. Encourage the children to use mathematical language. Discuss the size of the area on which children wish to base their own plan. Some children may need to concentrate on a relatively small area whilst others may be able to tackle a quite complex plan.

Extending the activity

Use a map or plan of your local area to stimulate further discussion about looking at areas from a spaceship. What would the school look like from above?

What if...?

A visitor arrived in school. Draw a plan of your school showing the important places a visitor would need to find.

ANSWERS

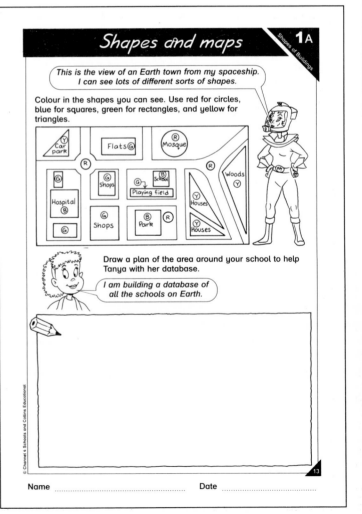

Shapes and maps

*This is the view of an Earth town from my spaceship.
I can see lots of different sorts of shapes.*

Colour in the shapes you can see. Use red for circles,
blue for squares, green for rectangles, and yellow for
triangles.

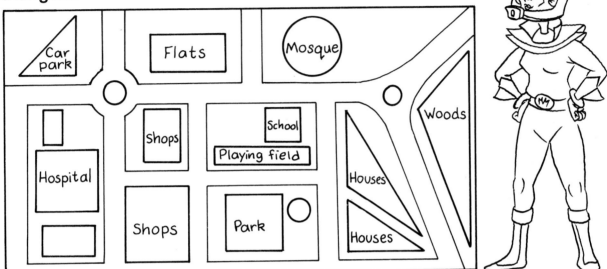

Draw a plan of the area around your school to help
Tanya with her database.

*I am building a database of
all the schools on Earth.*

13

Name .... Date ....

Sort the buildings

Mathematical content

The children will be asked to:
- ❏ look for shapes in real life situations
- ❏ describe 3-D shapes in terms of their properties
- ❏ use geometric language
- ❏ classify 3-D shapes

What you need

- ❏ a collection of 3-D shapes including a cuboid, a pyramid, a cone, a cylinder and a hemisphere
- ❏ large sheets of paper for making a poster

How to use the sheet

Have a collection of 3-D shapes available. Encourage the children to talk about the shapes and their properties. Do they know the mathematical names of any of them?

Extending the activity

Find examples of buildings in the locality which are different or unusual shapes. You could organise a class outing to look at some of these buildings and ask children to classify them according to their shape. Encourage children to think about what they might look like from above.

What if...?

You viewed a cuboid, a cone and a cylinder from above. Draw what you would see.

ANSWERS

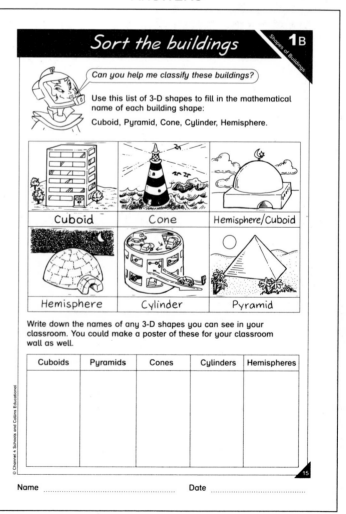

Sort the buildings

Can you help me classify these buildings?

Use this list of 3-D shapes to fill in the mathematical name of each building shape:

Cuboid, Pyramid, Cone, Cylinder, Hemisphere.

Cuboid

Write down the names of any 3-D shapes you can see in your classroom. You could make a poster of these for your classroom wall as well.

Cuboids	Pyramids	Cones	Cylinders	Hemispheres

Name .... Date ....

Wall patterns

Maths one

Mathematical content

The children will be asked to:
- ❐ develop and describe repeating patterns
- ❐ show their awareness of pattern
- ❐ use mathematical language
- ❐ look for pattern
- ❐ design 2-D patterns

What you need

- ❐ squared paper or copies of *General sheet 1* (for *Extending the activity*)

How to use the sheet

Look at the patterns on the sheet with the children. Ask the children to think of different ways of describing the patterns. After the patterns have been filled in look at them for symmetry and regularity. Ask which patterns look the best and why.

Extending the activity

Make some irregular brick patterns on squared paper or *General sheet 1*, using 2 squares for each brick shape. What do the children think about these patterns? Look at patterns around the school either in the brickwork or in tiles. The children could prepare a school 'Maths Trail', listing all the patterns they have found and asking friends to discover where in the school each one can be seen.

What if...?

You could use more than 2 colours to make wall patterns. Experiment with all the different patterns you can make.

ANSWERS

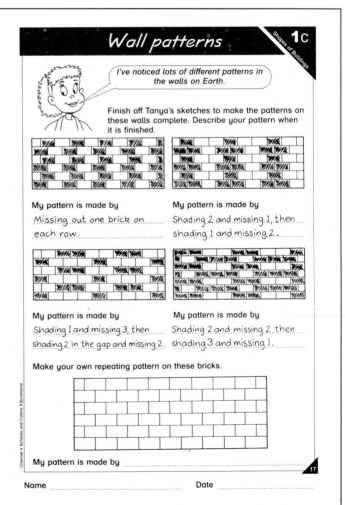

I've noticed lots of different patterns in the walls on Earth.

Finish off Tanya's sketches to make the patterns on these walls complete. Describe your pattern when it is finished.

My pattern is made by
Missing out one brick on each row.

My pattern is made by
Shading 2 and missing 1, then shading 1 and missing 2.

My pattern is made by
Shading 1 and missing 3, then shading 2 in the gap and missing 2.

My pattern is made by
Shading 2 and missing 2, then shading 3 and missing 1.

Make your own repeating pattern on these bricks.

My pattern is made by ....

Name .... Date ....

Wall patterns

I've noticed lots of different patterns in the walls on Earth.

Finish off Tanya's sketches to make the patterns on these walls complete. Describe your pattern when it is finished.

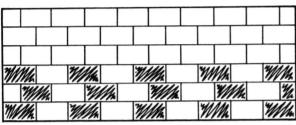

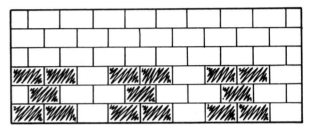

My pattern is made by

....

....

My pattern is made by

....

....

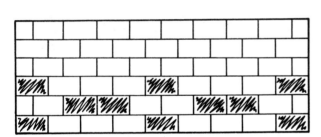

My pattern is made by

....

....

My pattern is made by

....

....

Make your own repeating pattern on these bricks.

My pattern is made by ....

Name ....   **Date** ....

Skyscrapers

Mathematical content

The children will be asked to:
- ❏ describe and represent shapes in terms of their location and movement
- ❏ measure quantities including length
- ❏ try different approaches to their mathematics to overcome difficulties
- ❏ use diagrams to show conclusions
- ❏ visualise shape and movement
- ❏ make 3-D shapes and transform them

What you need

- ❏ Multilink cubes or similar
- ❏ squared paper or copies of *General sheet 1* (for *Extending the activity*)

How to use the sheet

Make a sample of 1 of Tanya's models and discuss the 3 different views with the children. You might need to point out that the drawings do not convey perspective and so the cubes that appear to be on the same plane may actually be on a different plane. The children will only be able to tell if they have made a suitable model by checking each view.

Extending the activity

Ask the children to make skyscrapers of their own and draw them from different views. Their friends then have to use the drawings to try and work out the skyscrapers which their friends have made.

What if...?

You made a model twice the size of Tanya's? How many cubes do you think you would need? Draw your model here.

ANSWERS

Skyscrapers **1D**

Shapes of Buildings

I have made 3 different skyscrapers out of 8 Multilink cubes.

Tanya has drawn each of her skyscrapers from the top, from the front and from the side. Use her drawings to make the skyscrapers.

	Top	Front	Side
Skyscraper 1			
Skyscraper 2			
Skyscraper 3			

Make another skyscraper using 8 Multilink cubes. Draw its 3 views here:

	Top	Front	Side
My skyscraper			

How high is your skyscraper? ....

How wide is your skyscraper? ....

How deep is your skyscraper? ....

Name .... Date ....

Skyscrapers

I have made 3 different skyscrapers out of 8 Multilink cubes.

Tanya has drawn each of her skyscrapers from the top, from the front and from the side. Use her drawings to make the skyscrapers.

	Top	Front	Side
Skyscraper 1			
Skyscraper 2			
Skyscraper 3			

Make another skyscraper using 8 Multilink cubes.
Draw its 3 views here:

	Top	Front	Side
My skyscraper			

How high is your skyscraper? ....

How wide is your skyscraper? ....

How deep is your skyscraper? ....

Name .... Date ....

Nets of cubes

Mathematical content

The children will be asked to:

❐ look for the structure underlying properties of shapes
❐ use their understanding of the properties of 3-D shapes
❐ check their results
❐ search for pattern in their results and explain their reasoning
❐ visualise and describe shapes
❐ construct 3-D shapes

What you need

❐ sticky tape
❐ copies of *General sheet 2*
❐ a variety of boxes and packets (for *Extending the activity*)

How to use the sheet

Let the children try the sheet unaided. Copy *General sheet 2* for the children to cut up and tape together. When they have checked their guesses, ask if they were surprised by any they got wrong. Look for features shared by the nets which make cubes.

Extending the activity

Ask the children to open up different shaped boxes and explore the nets which are used to make cuboids and other 3-D shapes.

What if...?

You wanted to colour in the cubes so that no 2 joined faces are the same colour. What is the smallest number of colours you need to use?

ANSWERS

© Channel 4 Schools and Collins Educational

On Earth I noticed a special kind of cuboid called a cube. Every face of a cube is a square.

Some of these nets will make a cube when you fold them up and some will not. Put a tick by the ones you think will make a cube and a cross by those which won't.

Cut up a copy of the *Nets sheet* to see which of your guesses were correct. What does a net have to look like to fold into a cube?

....

....

Name .... **Date** ....

Building walls

Mathematical content

The children will be asked to:
- ❐ use and develop their understanding of patterns in the number system
- ❐ understand, learn and use basic number facts
- ❐ solve numerical problems in a real context
- ❐ measure lengths and areas
- ❐ explore factors of numbers

What you need

- ❐ Multilink cubes or similar
- ❐ squared paper or copies of *General sheet 1*

How to use the sheet

Provide 24 Multilink cubes and ask the children to make different walls with them. Also provide copies of *General sheet 1* for children who need to draw the walls in the second part of the activity. Encourage children to record the height and length of the wall as shown in the example.

Extending the activity

Collect all the different walls from the class after they have completed their sheets.

Compile the results to see if they have got all the different possibilities. Only at this point talk about factors and organising results. Choose other numbers and make lists of their factors.

What if...?

You chose any other number of bricks. What sorts of numbers would give you the most walls and what sorts of numbers would give you the fewest walls? Draw or list the walls. Explain your answers.

ANSWERS

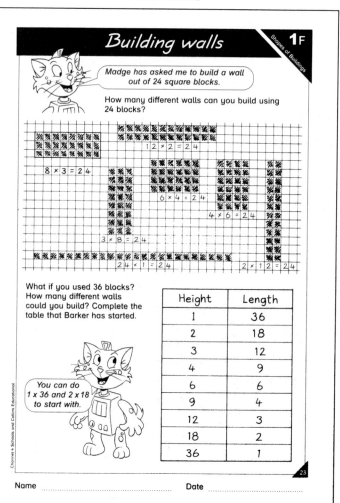

Building walls **1F** Shapes of Buildings

Madge has asked me to build a wall out of 24 square blocks.

How many different walls can you build using 24 blocks?

$12 \times 2 = 24$

$8 \times 3 = 24$

$6 \times 4 = 24$

$4 \times 6 = 24$

$3 \times 8 = 24$

$24 \times 1 = 24$

$2 \times 12 = 24$

What if you used 36 blocks? How many different walls could you build? Complete the table that Barker has started.

You can do 1 x 36 and 2 x 18 to start with.

Height	Length
1	36
2	18
3	12
4	9
6	6
9	4
12	3
18	2
36	1

Name .... Date ....

Building walls

Madge has asked me to build a wall out of 24 square blocks.

How many different walls can you build using 24 blocks?

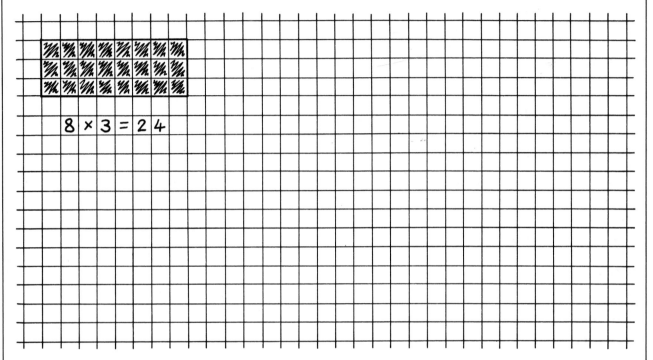

8 × 3 = 2 4

What if you used 36 blocks? How many different walls could you build? Complete the table that Barker has started.

Height	Length
1	36
2	18

You can do 1 x 36 and 2 x 18 to start with.

Name .... Date ....

Shapes of Buildings Wordsheet

Madge needs a mathematical dictionary to take back to her planet. Here are some words that you might recognise from your *Shapes of Buildings* worksheets. Write or draw in the boxes below to explain what the words mean so that Madge can add them to her dictionary.

circle	cone
cuboid	cylinder
hemisphere	rectangle
three-dimensional (3-D)	two-dimensional (2-D)

Patterns in Buildings

Setting the scene

Our inquisitive space crew look in more detail at buildings on Earth. Madge notices that several buildings have triangular features such as roofs, gable ends, windows and the sides of pyramids. This leads into an exploration of the properties of triangles, triangle numbers and eventually into examining square numbers.

The worksheets in this section are:

2A Roof triangles
classifying 2-D shapes

2B Making pyramids
constructing 3-D shapes

2C Trellis walk
problem solving

2D Numbers in triangles
number sequences

2E Triangle perimeters
shape and measurement

2F Square numbers
number sequences

Patterns in Buildings Wordsheet
mathematical language

Name .... **Date** ....

Roof triangles

Mathematical content

The children will be asked to:
- ❏ accurately describe and classify triangles
- ❏ recognise the geometric properties of triangles
- ❏ use appropriate mathematical language

What you need

- ❏ a collection of magazines (for *Extending the activity*)
- ❏ coloured pencils or crayons (red, blue, green and yellow)

How to use the sheet

Where have the children seen triangles in their environment? Discuss the properties and names of different types of triangles, the lengths of their sides and their angles.

Extending the activity

Ask the children to cut out any triangles they find in the magazines. Classify these triangles. Look for different shaped triangles in the classroom.

What if...?

> *You used triangles to make patterns. What triangle patterns can you design? Which sort of triangles make the best patterns?*

ANSWERS

Roof triangles

Here are lots of the roofs which we saw on our visit to Earth. They are all different sorts of triangles.

Help Madge classify her roofs.

Colour: equilateral triangles – red
          isosceles triangles – blue
          right-angled triangles – green
          scalene triangles – yellow

Finish off these sentences. They are to go in Madge's mathematical dictionary.

An equilateral triangle has ....

An isosceles triangle has ....

A right-angled triangle has ....

A scalene triangle has ....

Name ....   **Date** ....

Making pyramids

Mathematical content

The children will be asked to:
- ❏ visualise shapes and movement
- ❏ make 3-D shapes
- ❏ understand and use properties of 2-D and 3-D shapes
- ❏ choose and use appropriate mathematical instruments

What you need

- ❏ photocopy of nets on thin card
- ❏ sticky tape or glue
- ❏ protractors or pairs of compasses (for *Extending the activity*)

How to use the sheet

Photocopy the nets on to thin card. After the children have made the 2 square-based pyramids talk about the differences. Some children may be surprised that a pyramid does not always have its point directly above the centre of its base.

Extending the activity

Encourage some children to copy the nets themselves. They will need to use protractors to measure the angles or a pair of compasses to make sure they are accurate drawings of the nets.

What if...?

You wanted to make a net of a pyramid. What rules would you have to follow? Design nets for 2 more different square-based pyramids.

ANSWERS

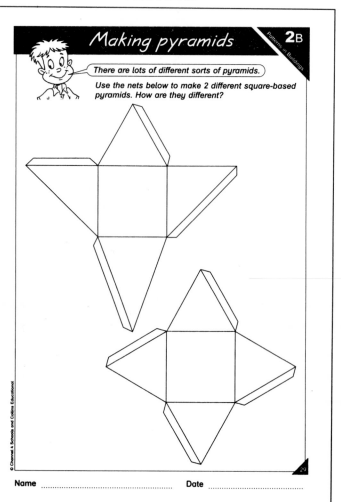

There are lots of different sorts of pyramids.

Use the nets below to make 2 different square-based pyramids. How are they different?

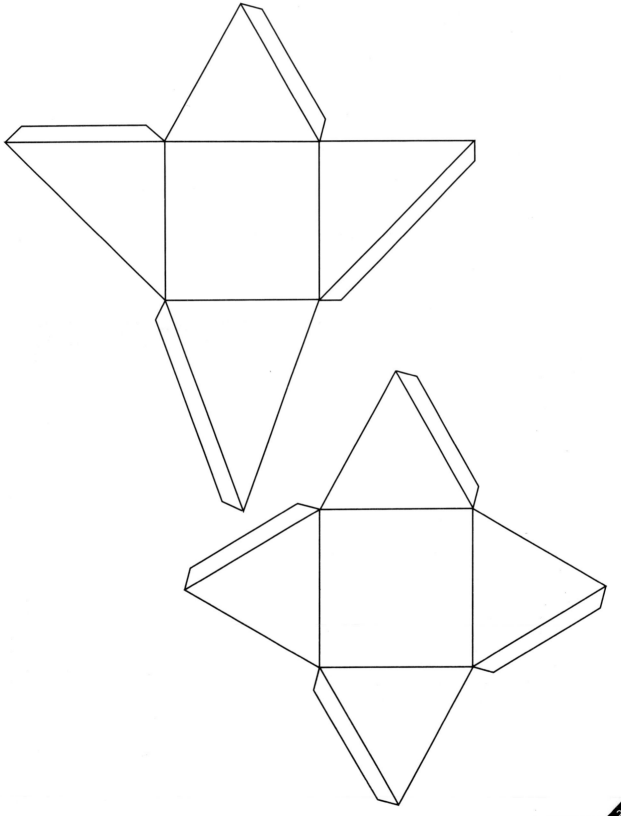

Name .... **Date** ....

Trellis walk

Mathematical content

The children will be asked to:
- ❐ give solutions which are appropriate to the context of the problem
- ❐ describe location and movement
- ❐ develop strategies for solving problems
- ❐ check results
- ❐ search for pattern in their results, trying out ideas of their own

What you need

- ❐ triangle dotty paper or copies of *General sheet 3*

How to use the sheet

Check the children understand the idea of always moving forwards across the trellis. Look for some routes which are allowed and not allowed. Encourage the children to use triangle dotty paper or *General sheet 3* to work out different routes before transferring their findings to the sheet. You can encourage the children to be systematic by asking questions such as, 'Have you got them all?', 'Are all your routes different?'.

Extending the activity

Explore different-sized trellises. What happens with a 4 x 4 trellis? What about a 5 x 5 trellis? Is the answer always the same? Try changing the rules and see how that affects the number of routes.

What if...?

> You could change the rule so the ladybird doesn't always move towards the aphid. How many ways across are there now?

ANSWERS

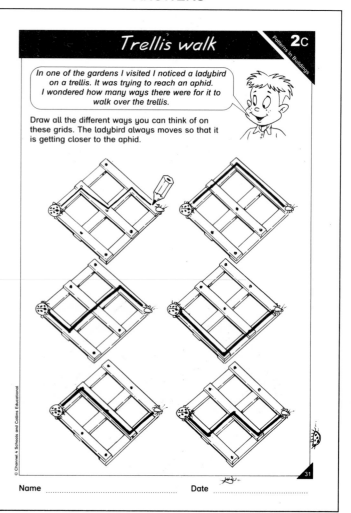

Name .... Date ....

In one of the gardens I visited I noticed a ladybird on a trellis. It was trying to reach an aphid. I wondered how many ways there were for it to walk over the trellis.

Draw all the different ways you can think of on these grids. The ladybird always moves so that it is getting closer to the aphid.

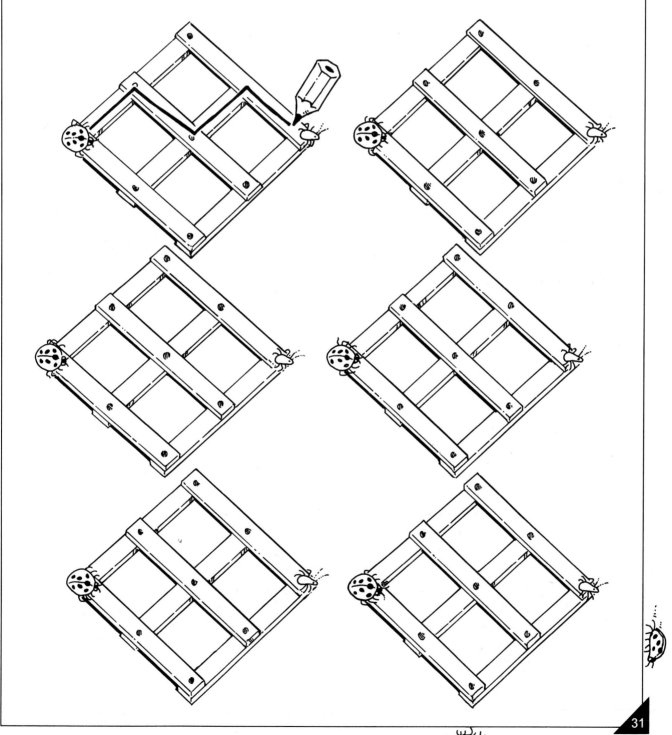

Name ....   Date ....

Numbers in triangles

Mathematical content

The children will be asked to:
- ❐ explore number sequences and generalise from observations
- ❐ search for pattern in number
- ❐ explain the reasoning behind their conjectures
- ❐ develop strategies for solving problems

What you need

- ❐ copies of *General sheet 4*

How to use the sheet

Discuss the way the triangles have been shaded. Look at the link between the shading and the addition of consecutive numbers. Ask the children to complete the grid. If children need triangle paper to continue the pattern have copies of *General sheet 4* available.

Extending the activity

As a follow-up, you can explore *triangle numbers*. The 1st triangle number is 1, the 2nd is 1 + 2 = 3, the 3rd is 1 + 2 + 3 = 6 and so on. This can be illustrated by forming triangles of dots or counters.

What if…?

You multiplied consecutive numbers together. What patterns would you find? Explore other patterns you can make with consecutive numbers.

ANSWERS

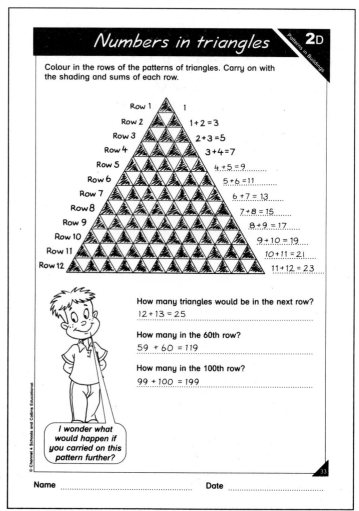

Colour in the rows of the patterns of triangles. Carry on with the shading and sums of each row.

Row 1 — 1
Row 2 — 1 + 2 = 3
Row 3 — 2 + 3 = 5
Row 4 — 3 + 4 = 7
Row 5 — 4 + 5 = 9
Row 6 — 5 + 6 = 11
Row 7 — 6 + 7 = 13
Row 8 — 7 + 8 = 15
Row 9 — 8 + 9 = 17
Row 10 — 9 + 10 = 19
Row 11 — 10 + 11 = 21
Row 12 — 11 + 12 = 23

How many triangles would be in the next row?
12 + 13 = 25

How many in the 60th row?
59 + 60 = 119

How many in the 100th row?
99 + 100 = 199

I wonder what would happen if you carried on this pattern further?

Name .... Date ....

Colour in the rows of the patterns of triangles. Carry on with the shading and sums of each row.

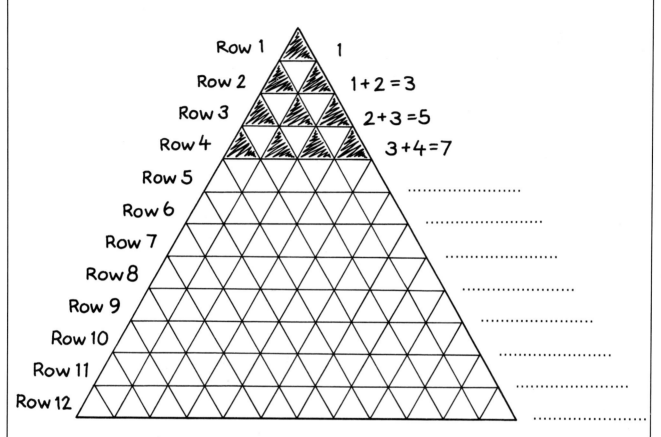

Row 1   1

Row 2   1 + 2 = 3

Row 3   2 + 3 = 5

Row 4   3 + 4 = 7

Row 5 ....

Row 6 ....

Row 7 ....

Row 8 ....

Row 9 ....

Row 10 ....

Row 11 ....

Row 12 ....

I wonder what would happen if you carried on this pattern further?

How many triangles would be in the next row?

....

How many in the 60th row?

....

How many in the 100th row?

....

33

Name .... **Date** ....

Triangle perimeters

Mathematical content

The children will be asked to:
- ❐ describe triangles in terms of their properties
- ❐ measure lengths
- ❐ use appropriate mathematical language when describing shapes
- ❐ use measuring instruments

What you need

- ❐ pairs of compasses (for the *What if...?* activity)

How to use the sheet

Check that children know the meaning of *perimeter* and remind them of the meaning *equilateral*, *isoceles*, *right-angled* and *scalene*.

Extending the activity

Create a table to look at all possible arrangements for the perimeters e.g. 1 1 10, 2 2 8 and so on. Discuss which arrangements will make triangles and why. Discuss the strategies for drawing up a table with all the possibilities for perimeters using whole or half numbers of cm for the side lengths.

What if...?

You made triangles each with a perimeter of 24 cm. How many different triangles could you make whose sides are all a whole number of cm long?

ANSWERS

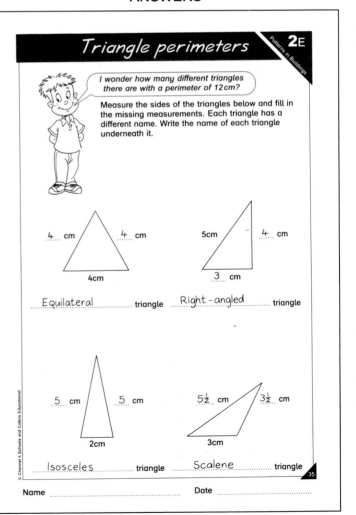

I wonder how many different triangles there are with a perimeter of 12cm?

Measure the sides of the triangles below and fill in the missing measurements. Each triangle has a different name. Write the name of each triangle underneath it.

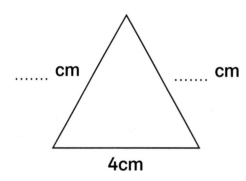

.... cm   .... cm

4cm

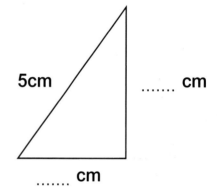

5cm   .... cm

.... cm

.... triangle

.... triangle

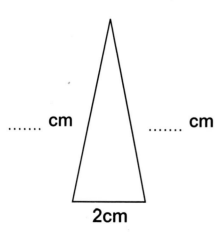

.... cm   .... cm

2cm

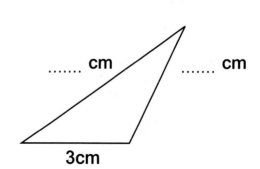

.... cm   .... cm

3cm

.... triangle

.... triangle

Name ....   Date ....

Square numbers

Mathematical content

The children will be asked to:
- ❑ explore number sequences and generalise from observations
- ❑ search for pattern in number
- ❑ explain the reasoning behind their conjectures
- ❑ develop strategies for solving problems
- ❑ know properties of numbers such as *even* and *odd*, and *square*

What you need

- ❑ squared paper or copies of *General sheet 1*

How to use the sheet

Look at the way the squares have been shaded on the sheet. Allow children to complete the pattern.

Extending the activity

Some children might want to continue the sequence on squared paper (*General sheet 1*). Remind children of words such as *odd*, *even* and *square* numbers. Allow children to devise their own definitions of words.

What if…?

You do the same activity but use cubes. The first shape has 1 cube, the next has 1 + 7 cubes, the next has 1 + 7 + 19 cubes. Explore this pattern further.

ANSWERS

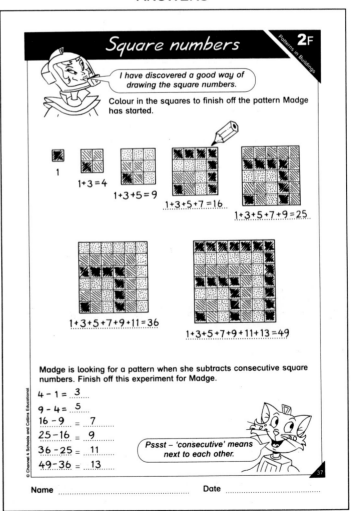

I have discovered a good way of drawing the square numbers.

Colour in the squares to finish off the pattern Madge has started.

1

1+3=4

1+3+5=9

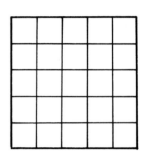

....

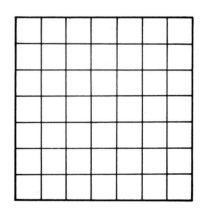

....

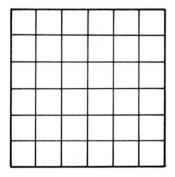

....

....

Madge is looking for a pattern when she subtracts consecutive square numbers. Finish off this experiment for Madge.

4 – 1 = ...

9 – 4 = ...

.... = ...

.... = ...

.... = ...

.... = ...

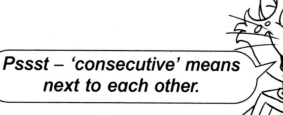

Pssst – 'consecutive' means next to each other.

Name .... **Date** ....

Patterns in Buildings Wordsheet

Madge needs a mathematical dictionary to take back to her planet. Here are some words that you might recognise from your *Patterns in Buildings* worksheets. Write or draw in the boxes below to explain what the words mean so that Madge can add them to her dictionary.

consecutive	equilateral triangle
isosceles triangle	perimeter
pyramid	right-angled triangle
scalene triangle	square number

Inside Shops

Setting the scene

Madge and the rest of the team visit a supermarket on Earth. They look at the layout of the supermarket and at the packaging, price and weights of the items sold there. Madge is particularly interested in the way fruits are stacked and this provides a good opportunity to look again at square and triangle numbers.

The worksheets in this section are:

Sorting shopping

Mathematical content

The children will be asked to:
- ❏ sort and classify objects describing the criteria they have chosen
- ❏ classify, using more than one criterion
- ❏ discuss their work using mathematical language
- ❏ experiment and try out ideas of their own

What you need

- ❏ set of Sorting shopping cards made from *General sheets 5* and *6*
- ❏ examples of board games (for *Extending the activity*)

How to use the sheet

Photocopy *General sheets 5* and *6* on to thin card. Allow children to play the games themselves. The games are called *Guess my card*, *Pairs*, *Sorting* and *My game* and the rules for each game are described on *General sheet 6*. The children can use the worksheet to help them summarise the activities in which they have been involved.

Extending the activity

Look at samples of other board games. What features are used in their design? What strategies are involved in playing the games?

What if…?

You designed a board game based around shopping. What would it look like?

ANSWERS

Sorting shopping **3A** Inside Shops

Did you enjoy playing games with the Sorting shopping cards?

Use this sheet to record some of the ways you used the cards.

Guess my card   <u>Example</u>

My card is <u>Samosas</u>

Clue 1 <u>They cost less than £1·00.</u>

Clue 2 <u>They are wrapped in a see-through packet.</u>

Clue 3 <u>You get two together.</u>

Pairs   <u>Example</u>

<u>Oranges</u> and <u>Grapefruit</u> are a pair

because <u>they are fruit.</u>

<u>Ice cream</u> and <u>Cat food</u> are a pair

because <u>they are cylinders.</u>

Sorting
I sorted the shopping like this: <u>Example</u>

<u>Cylinders</u>	<u>Cuboids</u>	<u>Pyramids</u>	<u>Spheres</u>
Tin of Tomatoes	Dry cat food	Tissues	Oranges
Ice cream	Tea	Pot pouri	Grapefruit
Bathroom Cleaner	Washing powder	Air freshner	Tomatoes
Cat food	Cornflakes	Candle	Cabbage
Biscuits	Dog food	Chocolate	String
Spaghetti	Fish fingers		Dogs Ball
Jam	Apple juice		

My game
The rules for my game are: <u>Example</u>

Take it in turns to pick a card. The person with the more expensive item can keep the cards. The winner is the person with the most cards at the end.

Name ....   Date ....

Sorting shopping

Did you enjoy playing games with the Sorting shopping cards?

Use this sheet to record some of the ways you used the cards.

Guess my card

My card is ....

Clue 1 ....

Clue 2 ....

Clue 3 ....

Pairs

.... and .... are a pair

because ....

.... and .... are a pair

because ....

Sorting
I sorted the shopping like this:

My game
The rules for my game are:

Name .... Date ....

Mathematical content

The children will be asked to:
- ❏ use and apply mathematics in practical situations and solve real life problems
- ❏ describe locations
- ❏ explain their reasoning
- ❏ obtain information needed to carry out their work

What you need

- ❏ scrap paper for brainstorming

How to use the sheet

Discuss the way that local shops are organised. What do they have in common? Talk about ways of describing articles in shops, e.g. *Dairy products*, *Household goods* etc. Encourage children to make a rough plan of their supermarket layout before drawing it on the worksheet.

Extending the activity

You could organise a trip to a local supermarket to look at how it is arranged and how the products are grouped. The children could list questions they want to answer, e.g. How many aisles are there? How many checkouts? and so on.

What if...?

You were asked to draw up a scale plan for a new supermarket. Draw your design.

ANSWERS

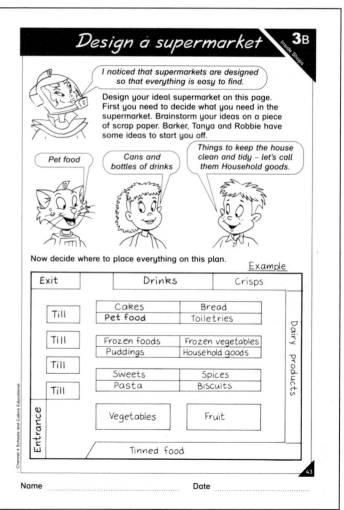

Design a supermarket

I noticed that supermarkets are designed so that everything is easy to find.

Design your ideal supermarket on this page. First you need to decide what you need in the supermarket. Brainstorm your ideas on a piece of scrap paper. Barker, Tanya and Robbie have some ideas to start you off.

Pet food

Cans and bottles of drinks

Things to keep the house clean and tidy – let's call them Household goods.

Now decide where to place everything on this plan.

Exit	Drinks	
Till	Pet food	
Till		
Till		
Till		
Entrance		

Name .... Date ....

Weighing apples

Mathematical content

The children will be asked to:

❑ use and apply their understanding of the pattern in the number system
❑ solve numerical problems involving systems of measurement
❑ use units of measurement of weight
❑ develop mathematical strategies to solve problems

What you need:

❑ sets of weights
❑ balance scales
❑ objects that weigh 100g, 200g, 500g and 1kg (for *Extending the activity*)

How to use the sheet

If possible, allow the children to try out the activity practically with some weights before using the worksheet. You may need to point out the example which uses a weight on the same side as the apples in order to balance the scales.

Extending the activity

Find items that weigh 100g, 200g, 500g and 1kg. Use these to estimate weights of other objects in the classroom.

What if…?

You used a set of weights such as 1, 2, 3, 4, 8 ounces and 1 pound. How many different amounts could you weigh?

ANSWERS

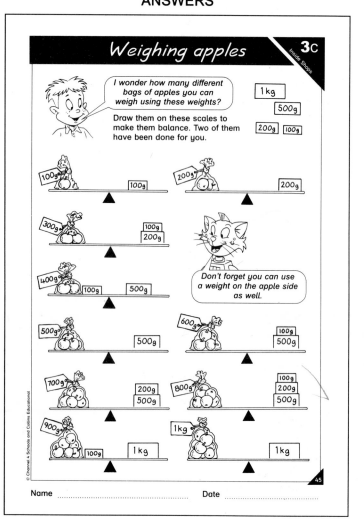

Name .... Date ....

I wonder how many different bags of apples you can weigh using these weights?

Draw them on these scales to make them balance. Two of them have been done for you.

1 kg

500g

200g 100g

Don't forget you can use a weight on the apple side as well.

Name ....   Date ....

Stacking apples

Mathematical content

The children will be asked to:
- ❏ use their understanding of relationships between numbers
- ❏ make conjectures and explain their reasoning
- ❏ explore number sequences and arrays
- ❏ explain and interpret pattern

What you need

- ❏ counters to model the problem

How to use the sheet

Allow the children to model the problem with counters before attempting the worksheet. Discuss the different patterns that children find within the table. *Note:* the numbers in each layer are called *triangle numbers*.

Extending the activity

Arrange a visit to a local fruit and vegetable shop or market stall. Ask the children to look at the different ways the produce is arranged. Why are different methods of stacking used?

What if...?

You added up consecutive triangle numbers. What patterns could you see then?

ANSWERS

Stacking apples **3D** Inside Shops

I looked at the way the apples were stacked. They were stacked in triangles like this:

Layer 1 — 1 apple
Layer 2 — 3 apples
Layer 3 — 6 apples

Complete this table to work out how many apples in the stack altogether.

Layer	Number of apples	Number in stack
1	1	1
2	3	1+ 3 = 4
3	6	1 + 3 + 6 = 10
4	10	1 + 3 + 6 +10 = 20
5	15	1+ 3 + 6 + 10 + 15 = 35
6	21	1+3+6 +10 +15 + 21 = 56
7	28	1+3+6 +10 +15 + 21 + 28 = 84
8	36	1+3+6 +10 +15 + 21 + 28 + 36 = 120
9	45	1+3+6 +10 +15 +21+28+36+45 = 165
10	55	1+3+6 +10 +15 +21+28+36+45+55 = 220

Write down anything you notice about the numbers in the table.

Example : The number of apples in each layer goes up by one more each time: 2, then 3, then 4, etc.

47

Name ....   Date ....

46

Stacking apples

*I looked at the way the apples were stacked.
They were stacked in triangles like this:*

Layer 1
1 apple

Layer 2
3 apples

Layer 3
6 apples

Complete this table to work out how many apples in the stack altogether.

Layer	Number of apples	Number in stack
1	1	1
2	3	1 + 3 = 4
3	6	1 + 3 + 6 = 10
4		
5		
6		
7		
8		
9		
10		

Write down anything you notice about the numbers in the table.

....

....

Name .... Date ....

Stacking oranges

Mathematical content

The children will be asked to:
- ❐ solve numerical problems in context
- ❐ appreciate relationships in number
- ❐ explore number sequences and arrays
- ❐ explain patterns and generalise relationships

What you need

- ❐ paper for rough work
- ❐ marbles and Plasticine

How to use the sheet

Allow the children to model the problem with real life items such as marbles and Plasticine before starting to record their findings. Encourage the children to look for different patterns in the table. Accept a range of responses.

Extending the activity

Use marbles and Plasticine to make stacks using different arrangements for the base: square, rectangular, triangular and so on.

What if...?

You stacked the oranges starting with different-sized rectangles. What number patterns would you find then?

ANSWERS

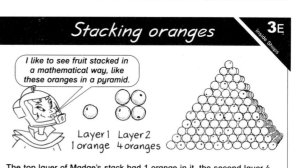

Stacking oranges — 3E — *Inside Shops*

I like to see fruit stacked in a mathematical way, like these oranges in a pyramid.

Layer 1 — 1 orange
Layer 2 — 4 oranges

The top layer of Madge's stack had 1 orange in it, the second layer 4, the third layer 9 and so on. Complete this table to show how many in the pyramid stack altogether.

Layer	Layer size	Number of oranges	Number in stack
1	1×1	1	1
2	2×2	4	1+4 = 5
3	3×3	9	1+4+9 = 14
4	4×4	16	1+4+9+16 = 30
5	5×5	25	1+4+9+16+25 = 55
6	6×6	36	1+4+9+16+25+36 = 91
7	7×7	49	1+4+9+16+25+36+49 = 140
8	8×8	64	1+4+9+16+25+36+49+64 = 204
9	9×9	81	1+4+9+16+25+36+49+64+81 = 285
10	10×10	100	1+4+9+16+25+36+49+64+81+100 = 385
11	11×11	121	1+4+9+16+25+36+49+64+81+100+121 = 506
12	12×12	144	1+4+9+16+25+36+49+64+81+100+121+144 = 650

Write down anything you notice about the numbers in this table.
Example: The number of oranges in each layer are
.... Square numbers. ....

49

Name .... Date ....

I like to see fruit stacked in a mathematical way, like these oranges in a pyramid.

Layer 1   Layer 2
1 orange   4 oranges

The top layer of Madge's stack had 1 orange in it, the second layer 4, the third layer 9 and so on. Complete this table to show how many in the pyramid stack altogether.

Layer	Layer size	Number of oranges	Number in stack
1	1 × 1	1	1
2	2 × 2	4	1 + 4 = 5
3	3 × 3	9	1 + 4 + 9 = 14
4			
5			
6			
7			
8			
9			
10			
11			
12			

Write down anything you notice about the numbers in this table.

....

....

Name ....   **Date** ....

Best buys

Mathematical content

The children will be asked to:

❒ use the four rules to solve problems involving money
❒ use and apply mathematics in real life situations
❒ use a range of computational methods
❒ use calculators and check their results for reasonableness
❒ choose sequences of computational methods and apply them accurately

What you need

❒ examples of different sizes of packages and jars
❒ calculators
❒ scrap paper for working out on
❒ a variety of shopping receipts (for *Extending the activity*)

How to use the sheet

Allow the children to work out, using a calculator, what they consider to be the best buy. Emphasise that exact answers are not necessary – this will encourage approximation and estimation. When the children have been working at the problem for a while, discuss their different solutions.

Extending the activity

Collect receipts from children's shopping trips with their parents. Look at the receipts and discuss the information that can be found on them. Ask them to make up questions for each other using these receipts.

What if...?

You had to decide the sizes for tins of beans. What sizes would you choose and what would they cost?

ANSWERS

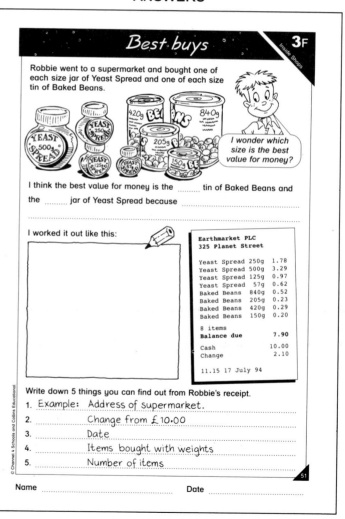

Robbie went to a supermarket and bought one of each size jar of Yeast Spread and one of each size tin of Baked Beans.

I wonder which size is the best value for money?

I think the best value for money is the .... tin of Baked Beans and

the .... jar of Yeast Spread because ....

....

I worked it out like this:

```
Earthmarket PLC
325 Planet Street

Yeast Spread 250g    1.78
Yeast Spread 500g    3.29
Yeast Spread 125g    0.97
Yeast Spread  57g    0.62
Baked Beans   840g    0.52
Baked Beans   205g    0.23
Baked Beans   420g    0.29
Baked Beans   150g    0.20

8 items
Balance due          7.90

Cash                10.00
Change               2.10

11.15 17 July 94
```

Write down 5 things you can find out from Robbie's receipt.

1. ....

2. ....

3. ....

4. ....

5. ....

Name ....   Date ....

Inside Shops Wordsheet

Madge needs a mathematical dictionary to take back to her planet. Here are some words that you might recognise from your *Inside Shops* worksheets. Write or draw in the boxes below to explain what the words mean so that Madge can add them to her dictionary.

balance	gram (g)
kilogram (kg)	layer
pair	plan
size	value for money

Living Indoors

Setting the scene

Madge is interested in the daily life of her Earthling friends and she pays a visit to a house where she looks at number patterns. While Barker is busy dreaming about milk deliveries, Tanya is working out how much it would cost to feed him on Earth. After all this activity our industrious team work up an appetite for pizzas. But what toppings should they choose and how should they share the pizzas out?

The worksheets in this section are:

4A Delivering milk
doubling and trebling

4B Number 7
multiplication patterns

4C Pizzas
permutations

4D Stairs
number patterns

4E Pizza fractions
fractions

4F Keeping pets
money

Living Indoors Wordsheet
mathematical language

Name .... Date ....

Delivering milk

Mathematical content

The children will be asked to:
- ❐ solve numerical problems set in a context
- ❐ apply their understanding of the relationship between numbers
- ❐ explore number sequences involving doubling and trebling
- ❐ choose sequences of computational methods appropriate to solving problems

What you need

- ❐ calculators

How to use the sheet

Discuss ways of doubling – repeated addition or multiplying by two. Ask children to guess how many pints will be delivered altogether, before they work it out. Make comparisons between the children's answers and their estimates.

Extending the activity

How much milk does the class drink each day/week? How much does it cost? What about the school? How many crates are delivered to the school every day?

What if...?

The delivery was trebled at each house. How many pints altogether this time?

ANSWERS

I had a wonderful dream about a milkman delivering milk to the houses in a street. He delivered 1 pint to the first house, 2 to the second and so on, doubling the amount he left each time. I lived in the last house on the street.

Fill in the amount of milk delivered to each house in the street to work out how much milk Barker might have to drink in his dream.

How many crates would be needed for Barker's street?

There are 32 pints in a crate.

Name .... **Date** ....

Number 7

Mathematical content

The children will be asked to:
- ❐ learn basic number facts
- ❐ examine structures and relationships within the number system
- ❐ examine relationships between numbers
- ❐ read, write and order whole numbers
- ❐ explore number sequences and arrays
- ❐ explain and interpret number patterns

What you need

- ❐ calculators
- ❐ copies of *General sheet 7* (for the *What if...?* activity)

How to use the sheet

Check that the children can remember the pattern of the multiples of 7. Revise the 7 times table and/or use the constant function on a calculator to list the multiples of 7. Encourage the children to guess the types of patterns which will appear before they fill in the squares.

Extending the activity

Use the constant function on the calculator to create multiples by repeated addition. Encourage children to look at patterns like 13, 19 etc. using the calculator.

What if...?

You used multiples of different numbers. What patterns do you get? Which number patterns look most like those you get with multiples of 7?

ANSWERS

Number 7 **4B**

Living Indoors

7 appeared a lot in the house I visited. It was number 7 on the street, there were 7 steps to the front door, 1 of the children in the house was 7 and, there were 7 rooms altogether.

Use the number grids below to explore the patterns Madge could get by shading in multiples of 7. The first one has been started for you.

Write about one of the patterns you found.

Example: The grid which is 8 long has 2 diagonals.

Name .... Date ....

57

7 appeared a lot in the house I visited. It was number 7 on the street, there were 7 steps to the front door, 1 of the children in the house was 7 and, there were 7 rooms altogether.

Use the number grids below to explore the patterns Madge could get by shading in multiples of 7. The first one has been started for you.

1	2	3	4	5	6	7	8	9
10	11	12	13	14	15	16	17	18
19	20	21	22	23	24	25	26	27
28	29	30	31	32	33	34	35	36
37	38	39	40	41	42	43	44	45
46	47	48	49	50	51	52	53	54
55	56	57	58	59	60	61	62	63
64	65	66	67	68	69	70	71	72
73	74	75	76	77	78	79	80	81
82	83	84	85	86	87	88	89	90
91	92	93	94	95	96	97	98	99

1	2	3	4	5	6	7	8	9	10
11	12	13	14	15	16	17	18	19	20
21	22	23	24	25	26	27	28	29	30
31	32	33	34	35	36	37	38	39	40
41	42	43	44	45	46	47	48	49	50
51	52	53	54	55	56	57	58	59	60
61	62	63	64	65	66	67	68	69	70
71	72	73	74	75	76	77	78	79	80
81	82	83	84	85	86	87	88	89	90
91	92	93	94	95	96	97	98	99	100

1	2	3	4	5	6	7
8	9	10	11	12	13	14
15	16	17	18	19	20	21
22	23	24	25	26	27	28
29	30	31	32	33	34	35
36	37	38	39	40	41	42
43	44	45	46	47	48	49
50	51	52	53	54	55	56
57	58	59	60	61	62	63
64	65	66	67	68	69	70
71	72	73	74	75	76	77
78	79	80	81	82	83	84
85	86	87	88	89	90	91
92	93	94	95	96	97	98

1	2	3	4	5	6	7	8
9	10	11	12	13	14	15	16
17	18	19	20	21	22	23	24
25	26	27	28	29	30	31	32
33	34	35	36	37	38	39	40
41	42	43	44	45	46	47	48
49	50	51	52	53	54	55	56
57	58	59	60	61	62	63	64
65	66	67	68	69	70	71	72
73	74	75	76	77	78	79	80
81	82	83	84	85	86	87	88
89	90	91	92	93	94	95	96

Write about one of the patterns you found.

....

....

Name .... **Date** ....

Pizzas

Mathematical content

The children will be asked to:
- ❐ present information and results clearly
- ❐ develop mathematical strategies to overcome problems
- ❐ work systematically to solve problems
- ❐ explain their results
- ❐ search for a pattern in their results

What you need

- ❐ scrap paper to model the problem
- ❐ copies of *General sheet 8*

How to use the sheet

Use *General Sheet 8* for the children to experiment with pizza toppings. Ask the children how many different pizzas they think are possible. Using these toppings, arrange them to make different pizzas. Ask the children how they can check that they have got all the possiblities. Compare their answers with their estimates.

Extending the activity

Survey the class to find out the children's favourite toppings. Can they devise 2 or 3 pizzas that would satisfy everybody?

What if...?

Each person had at least 3 toppings. How many different pizzas could you make? Explore the problem using different numbers of toppings.

ANSWERS

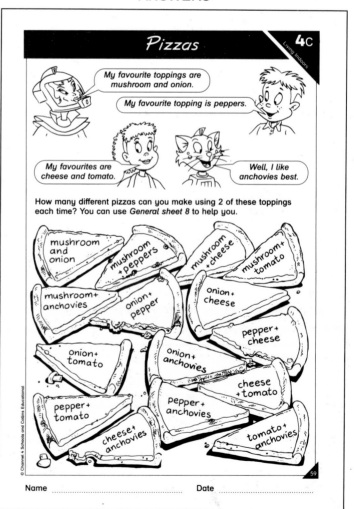

My favourite toppings are mushroom and onion.

My favourite topping is peppers.

My favourites are cheese and tomato.

Well, I like anchovies best.

How many different pizzas can you make using 2 of these toppings each time? You can use *General sheet 8* to help you.

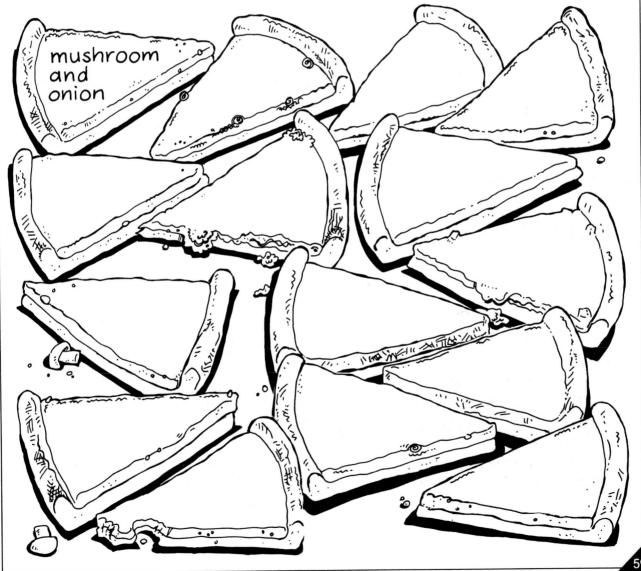

mushroom and onion

Name .... **Date** ....

Stairs

Mathematical content

The children will be asked to:
- ❒ break a problem down into steps to solve it
- ❒ make conjectures of their own and explain their reasoning
- ❒ search for a pattern in their results
- ❒ explore number sequences and arrays
- ❒ develop mathematical strategies to solve a problem

What you need

- ❒ copies of *General sheet 9* for working out on
- ❒ Multilink cubes (for *Extending the activity*)

How to use the sheet

Discuss the pictures of Barker showing the alternative ways to jump down 3 steps. Give the children *General Sheet 9* to work out the different ways of coming down stairs before recording on the worksheet. Ask the children to describe any patterns or generalisations they have found in their patterns.

Extending the activity

Suggest the children make staircases out of Multilink cubes. How many cubes do they use for each set of stairs?

What if...?

Barker jumped down 8 steps, or 10 steps or 100 steps. Can you find a quick way of working out the answers?

ANSWERS

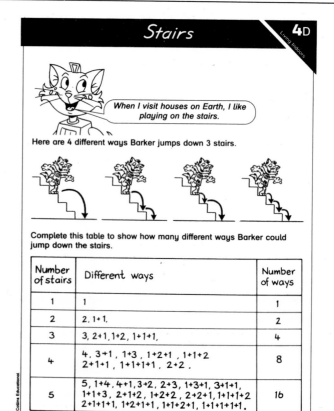

Stairs

4D

Living Indoors

When I visit houses on Earth, I like playing on the stairs.

Here are 4 different ways Barker jumps down 3 stairs.

Complete this table to show how many different ways Barker could jump down the stairs.

Number of stairs	Different ways	Number of ways
1	1	1
2	2, 1+1,	2
3	3, 2+1, 1+2, 1+1+1,	4
4	4, 3+1, 1+3, 1+2+1, 1+1+2 2+1+1, 1+1+1+1, 2+2.	8
5	5, 1+4, 4+1, 3+2, 2+3, 1+3+1, 3+1+1, 1+1+3, 2+1+2, 1+2+2, 2+2+1, 1+1+1+2 2+1+1+1, 1+2+1+1, 1+1+2+1, 1+1+1+1+1.	16

Write about anything you noticed about the numbers in the table.

..The number of ways doubles each time you go up.. ..one stair...

Name .... Date ....

When I visit houses on Earth, I like playing on the stairs.

Here are 4 different ways Barker jumps down 3 stairs.

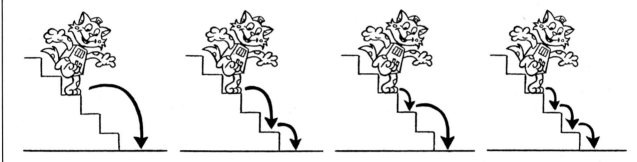

Complete this table to show how many different ways Barker could jump down the stairs.

Number of stairs	Different ways	Number of ways
1	1	1
2	2, 1+1,	2
3	3, 2+1, 1+2, 1+1+1,	4
4		
5		

Write about anything you noticed about the numbers in the table.

....

....

Name ....   **Date** ....

Pizza fractions

Mathematical content

The children will be asked to:
- ❏ solve numerical problems in real life contexts
- ❏ learn basic number facts
- ❏ explore numbers including fractions
- ❏ search for pattern in their results and explain their results
- ❏ use fractions to describe and compare parts of a whole

What you need

- ❏ copies of *General Sheet 10* (Pizza fractions)
- ❏ protractors (for *Extending the activity*)

How to use the sheet

Ask how the children would share out pizzas between groups. Use *General sheet 10* to do some sharing out between groups of children. When the children understand the problem practically give them the worksheet.

Extending the activity

The children could draw circles and use protractors to divide a pizza accurately into portions. Record the angles needed each time.

What if...?

> There were more people, or more pizzas. Make up some problems of your own.

ANSWERS

Pizza fractions — 4E — Living Indoors

My controller is coming to visit so I need to work out how we can share out pizzas for tea.

Help Madge work out how much pizza everyone will get.

Number of pizzas	Madge	Madge Robbie	Madge Robbie Tanya	Madge Robbie Tanya Barker	Madge Robbie Tanya Barker Controller
1	1	$\frac{1}{2}$	$\frac{1}{3}$	$\frac{1}{4}$	$\frac{1}{5}$
2	2	1	$\frac{2}{3}$	$\frac{1}{2}$	$\frac{2}{5}$
3	3	$1\frac{1}{2}$	1	$\frac{3}{4}$	$\frac{3}{5}$
4	4	2	$1\frac{1}{3}$	1	$\frac{4}{5}$
5	5	$2\frac{1}{2}$	$1\frac{2}{3}$	$1\frac{1}{4}$	1

Psst - ask your teacher for some blank pizzas to help you work this out.

I noticed some patterns in the table.

Write about any patterns you noticed.

Example: You add the fraction in the top row on each time as you go down.

Name .... Date ....

My controller is coming to visit so I need to work out how we can share out pizzas for tea.

Help Madge work out how much pizza everyone will get.

Number of pizzas	Madge	Madge Robbie	Madge Robbie Tanya	Madge Robbie Tanya Barker	Madge Robbie Tanya Barker Controller
1	1	$\frac{1}{2}$	$\frac{1}{3}$	$\frac{1}{4}$	$\frac{1}{5}$
2	2	1			
3					
4					
5					

Psst - ask your teacher for some blank pizzas to help you work this out.

I noticed some patterns in the table.

Write about any patterns you noticed.

....

....

Name .... **Date** ....

Keeping pets

Mathematical content

The children will be asked to:
- ❏ solve numerical problems in a real context
- ❏ estimate and approximate to check results are sensible
- ❏ use the four rules to solve problems involving money
- ❏ choose sequences of appropriate computational methods
- ❏ check results by different methods

What you need

- ❏ calculators
- ❏ scrap paper for working out

How to use the sheet

Get the children to look at all the information on the worksheet and check that they are clear about the information given there. Ask them to estimate the daily costs of keeping each animal. Talk about how you can use this information to work out weekly costs. Talk about rounding to the nearest penny – rounding up, because over-estimating is better than under-estimating.

Extending the activity

Ask the children what sorts of pets they have. How much does it cost to keep their pet for a week?

What if…?

You could create your own pet food. What information would you put on the label?

ANSWERS

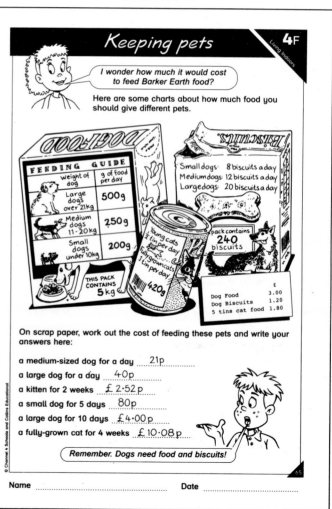

I wonder how much it would cost to feed Barker Earth food?

Here are some charts about how much food you should give different pets.

DOG FOOD

FEEDING	GUIDE
Weight of dog	g of food per day
Large dogs over 21kg	500g
Medium dogs 11-20kg	250g
Small dogs under 10kg	200g

THIS PACK CONTAINS 5kg

Young cats ½ tin per day
Fully grown cats 1 tin per day
420g

BISCUITS

Small dogs: 8 biscuits a day
Medium dogs: 12 biscuits a day
Large dogs: 20 biscuits a day

pack contains **240** biscuits

	£
Dog Food	3.00
Dog Biscuits	1.20
5 tins cat food	1.80

On scrap paper, work out the cost of feeding these pets and write your answers here:

a medium-sized dog for a day ....

a large dog for a day ....

a kitten for 2 weeks ....

a small dog for 5 days ....

a large dog for 10 days ....

a fully-grown cat for 4 weeks ....

Remember. Dogs need food and biscuits!

Name ....   Date ....

Living Indoors Wordsheet

Madge needs a mathematical dictionary to take back to her planet. Here are some words that you might recognise from your *Living Indoors* worksheets. Write or draw in the boxes below to explain what the words mean so that Madge can add them to her dictionary.

chart	cost
double	first
grid	multiple
pattern	second

Patterns in the Home

Setting the scene

Madge and her team are busy investigating patterns, especially those with lines of symmetry. They look at all sorts of different patterns: Rangoli, Yoruba and even snowflakes. Meanwhile Barker, who is also looking for symmetry, is busy cutting objects in half to test out his theory!

The worksheets in this section are:

5A   Symmetry in the home
symmetry

5B   Collecting patterns
classifying 2-D shapes

5C   Rangoli patterns
symmetry

5D   Rod spiral
number patterns

5E   Yoruba patterns
using and applying maths

5F   Snowflakes
problem solving

Patterns in the Home Wordsheet
mathematical language

Symmetry in the home

Mathematical content

The children will be asked to:
- ☐ describe shapes in terms of their location
- ☐ visualise and describe shapes and movements
- ☐ recognise reflective symmetry
- ☐ transform 2-D shapes by reflection

What you need

- ☐ tracing paper

How to use the sheet

Ask the children to use the tracing paper to trace one half of the picture. By reversing the tracing paper the children can complete the picture.

Extending the activity

Ask the children to draw objects from around the classroom which have a line of symmetry. They can then devise worksheets such as the one given here, for each other.

What if…?

You could only use letters of the alphabet which have a single line of symmetry. What messages could you write? What could you write if you could only use letters with 2 lines of symmetry?

ANSWERS

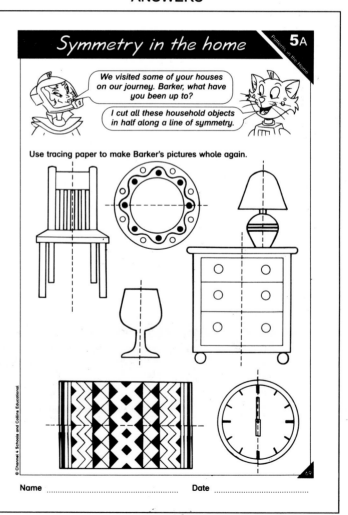

We visited some of your houses on our journey. Barker, what have you been up to?

I cut all these household objects in half along a line of symmetry.

Use tracing paper to make Barker's pictures whole again.

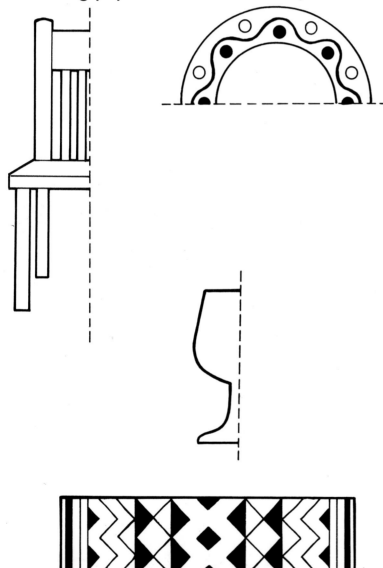

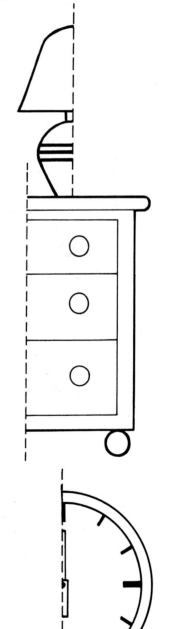

Name .... **Date** ....

Collecting patterns

Mathematical content

The children will be asked to:
- ❏ use geometrical language
- ❏ describe shapes and their properties
- ❏ classify shapes and patterns
- ❏ construct and describe repeating patterns

What you need

- ❏ collections of patterns (for *Extending the activity*)

How to use the sheet

Look around the classroom for examples of patterns and discuss how these may be classified according to the categories on the worksheet. Children may need reassuring that patterns may fit into more than one category. Encourage children to think of further categories they could use to classify patterns.

Extending the activity

Ask the class to collect as many of their favourite patterns as they can. Then ask groups to sort them in as many different ways as possible. List all the different categories. Discuss ways of recording, such as Venn diagrams, Carroll diagrams etc.

What if...?

You designed a pattern for the walls in your classroom. What would it look like?

ANSWERS

Collecting patterns 5B
Patterns in the Home

I visited some schools to look for patterns to add to my database. Help me by collecting some patterns from your school.

Draw any patterns you can find in your classroom or around the school in the spaces below.

Patterns with squares
Examples
Carpet Tiles
Windows

Patterns with triangles
Roofs

Patterns with curved lines
Windows

Another pattern
Hall floor

Which is your favourite pattern? Describe it here.

Name .... Date ....

Collecting patterns

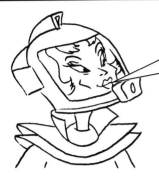

I visited some schools to look for patterns to add to my database. Help me by collecting some patterns from your school.

Draw any patterns you can find in your classroom or around the school in the spaces below.

Patterns with squares

Patterns with triangles

Patterns with curved lines

Another pattern

Which is your favourite pattern? Describe it here.

Name .... Date ....

Rangoli patterns

Mathematical content

The children will be asked to:
- ❐ explore the patterns which underlie properties of shapes
- ❐ construct 2-D patterns with accuracy
- ❐ recognise and use reflective symmetry
- ❐ use transformations to create repeating patterns

What you need

- ❐ copies of *General sheet 11* (for the *What if...?* activity)

How to use the sheet

If the children are unsure where to start, remind them that the pattern they make can be reflected both vertically and horizontally. Encourage the children to use their imagination but remain practical when they are designing their own pattern.

Extending the activity

Encourage the children to research different Rangoli patterns and explore them for mathematical properties. There may be children within your class who can share their expertise, or whose parents may be willing to do so.

What if...?

You needed a design with 4 lines of symmetry. Draw your design on dotty paper (General sheet 11) and stick it on this sheet.

ANSWERS

5c

Patterns in the Home

Rangoli patterns

In one of the houses I visited I saw some patterns called Rangoli patterns. The one I have started to copy here has 2 lines of symmetry but I didn't have time to finish it.

Finish off Robbie's pattern for him and colour it carefully.

Use these dots to create your own Rangoli pattern.

Name .... Date ....

Rangoli patterns

In one of the houses I visited I saw some patterns called Rangoli patterns. The one I have started to copy here has 2 lines of symmetry but I didn't have time to finish it.

Finish off Robbie's pattern for him and colour it carefully.

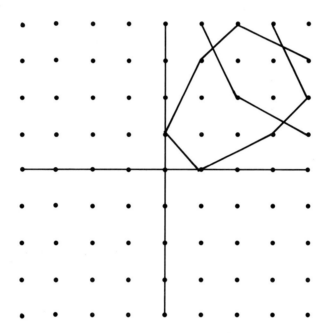

Use these dots to create your own Rangoli pattern.

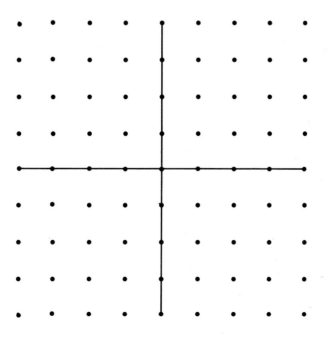

Name ....   **Date** ....

Rod spiral

Mathematical content

The children will be asked to:
- ❑ describe shapes and patterns in terms of their location
- ❑ explain their reasoning
- ❑ make 2-D shapes and patterns
- ❑ use geometrical language
- ❑ explore number sequences and arrays
- ❑ find areas, using counting methods

What you need

- ❑ Cuisenaire Rods or similar
- ❑ coloured pencils

How to use the sheet

If possible use Cuisenaire Rods to show how to build up the pattern started on the sheet. When the children see how the spiral forms, they can continue it, using coloured pencils. If they have difficulty explaining the pattern of colours they have used in the spiral, help them by asking how they knew when to use a new colour.

Extending the activity

Children could design other patterns with Cuisenaire Rods. Encourage them to make up their own rules, e.g. the patterns must cover a total of 100 units, or you can only use 2 rods of each type and so on.

What if...?

You wanted to make a spiral using triangles. How would you do it?

ANSWERS

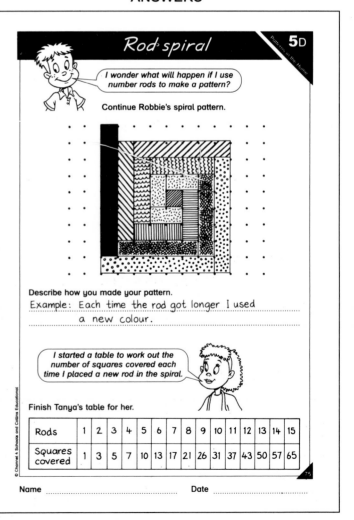

Rod spiral

I wonder what will happen if I use number rods to make a pattern?

Continue Robbie's spiral pattern.

Describe how you made your pattern.
Example: Each time the rod got longer I used a new colour.

I started a table to work out the number of squares covered each time I placed a new rod in the spiral.

Finish Tanya's table for her.

Rods	1	2	3	4	5	6	7	8	9	10	11	12	13	14	15
Squares covered	1	3	5	7	10	13	17	21	26	31	37	43	50	57	65

Name .... Date ....

Rod spiral

I wonder what will happen if I use number rods to make a pattern?

Continue Robbie's spiral pattern.

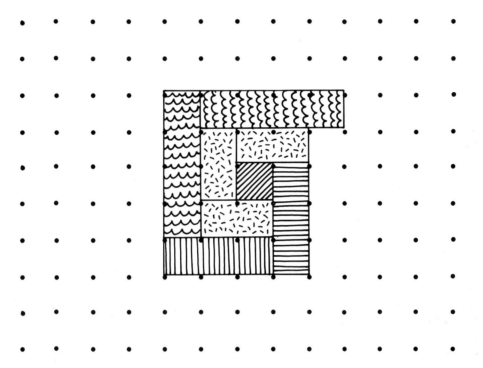

Describe how you made your pattern.

....

....

I started a table to work out the number of squares covered each time I placed a new rod in the spiral.

Finish Tanya's table for her.

Rods	1	2	3	4	5	6	7	8	9	10	11	12	13	14	15
Squares covered	1	3	5												

Name .... Date ....

Yoruba patterns

Mathematical content

The children will be asked to:
- ❏ describe and represent shapes in terms of their location and movement
- ❏ search for pattern in their results
- ❏ transform 2-D shapes by translation, reflection and rotation
- ❏ create and describe repeating patterns

What you need

- ❏ copies of *General sheet 12*

How to use the sheet

Photocopy *General sheet 12* and cut it up to provide the children with tiles for the activity. Children can then either stick the tiles down or copy the patterns they devise on to the worksheet. Encourage the children to look for symmetry in their patterns and to investigate the patterns which do not have symmetrical properties.

Extending the activity

Use blank squares and ask the children to design a pattern within the square. Make several copies of this pattern and use it to create a patchwork.

What if...?

You used hexagonal and square tiles. What sorts of repeating patterns could you make? Draw your favourites here.

ANSWERS

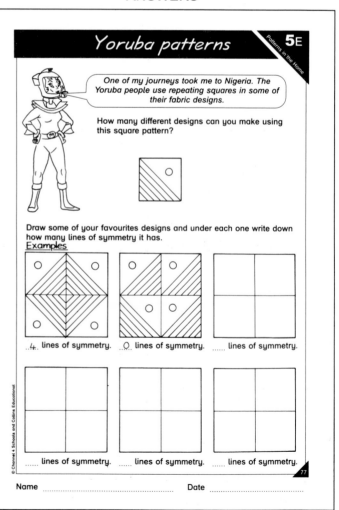

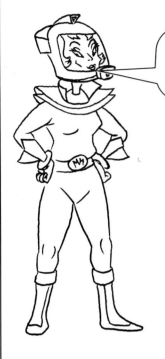

One of my journeys took me to Nigeria. The Yoruba people use repeating squares in some of their fabric designs.

How many different designs can you make using this square pattern?

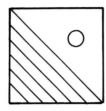

Draw some of your favourites designs and under each one write down how many lines of symmetry it has.

...... lines of symmetry. ...... lines of symmetry. ...... lines of symmetry.

...... lines of symmetry. ...... lines of symmetry. ...... lines of symmetry.

Name .... **Date** ....

Snowflakes

Mathematical content

The children will be asked to:
- ❏ search for pattern in their results and explain their reasoning
- ❏ make conjectures based on evidence
- ❏ explore number sequences and arrays
- ❏ explain number patterns

What you need

- ❏ Multilink cubes or similar
- ❏ squared paper or copies of *General Sheet 1* (for *Extending the activity*)

How to use this sheet

Use Multilink cubes to help children see how the pattern is built up. Once they have the idea they can continue the pattern on the worksheet. Encourage the children to use the symmetry of the pattern to help them complete it.

Extending the activity

The children can use the Multilink cubes to design other patterns which grow out like snowflakes. They can then use squared paper or *General sheet 1* to draw their patterns and explore any number sequences which they find within their patterns.

What if...?

You used Multilink cubes to make a 3-D snowflake. What number patterns are formed then?

ANSWERS

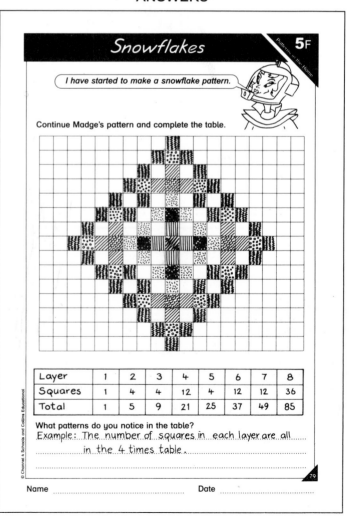

Snowflakes 5F

Patterns in the Home

I have started to make a snowflake pattern.

Continue Madge's pattern and complete the table.

Layer	1	2	3	4	5	6	7	8
Squares	1	4	4	12	4	12	12	36
Total	1	5	9	21	25	37	49	85

What patterns do you notice in the table?
Example: The number of squares in each layer are all in the 4 times table.

....

Name .... Date ....

Snowflakes

I have started to make a snowflake pattern.

Continue Madge's pattern and complete the table.

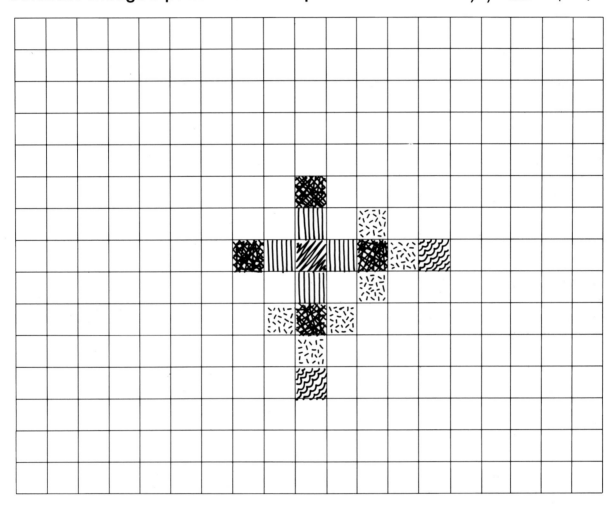

Layer	1	2	3	4	5	6	7	8
Squares	1	4	4	12				
Total	1	5	9	21				

What patterns do you notice in the table?

....

....

....

Name .... **Date** ....

Patterns in the Home Wordsheet

Madge needs a mathematical dictionary to take back to her planet. Here are some words that you might recognise from your *Patterns in the Home* worksheets. Write or draw in the boxes below to explain what the words mean so that Madge can add them to her dictionary.

curved	database
design	repeating
spiral	symmetry
total	whole

General sheets

General sheet 1
Squared paper

General sheet 2
Nets of cubes

General sheet 3
Triangle dotty paper

General sheet 4
Triangle paper

General sheet 5
Shopping cards

General sheet 6
Shopping cards and rules

General sheet 7
Number grids

General sheet 8
Pizza toppings

General sheet 9
Stairs

General sheet 10
Pizza fractions

General sheet 11
Square dotty paper

General sheet 12
Yoruba patterns

What if...?

Pupil record sheet

Name .... **Date** ....

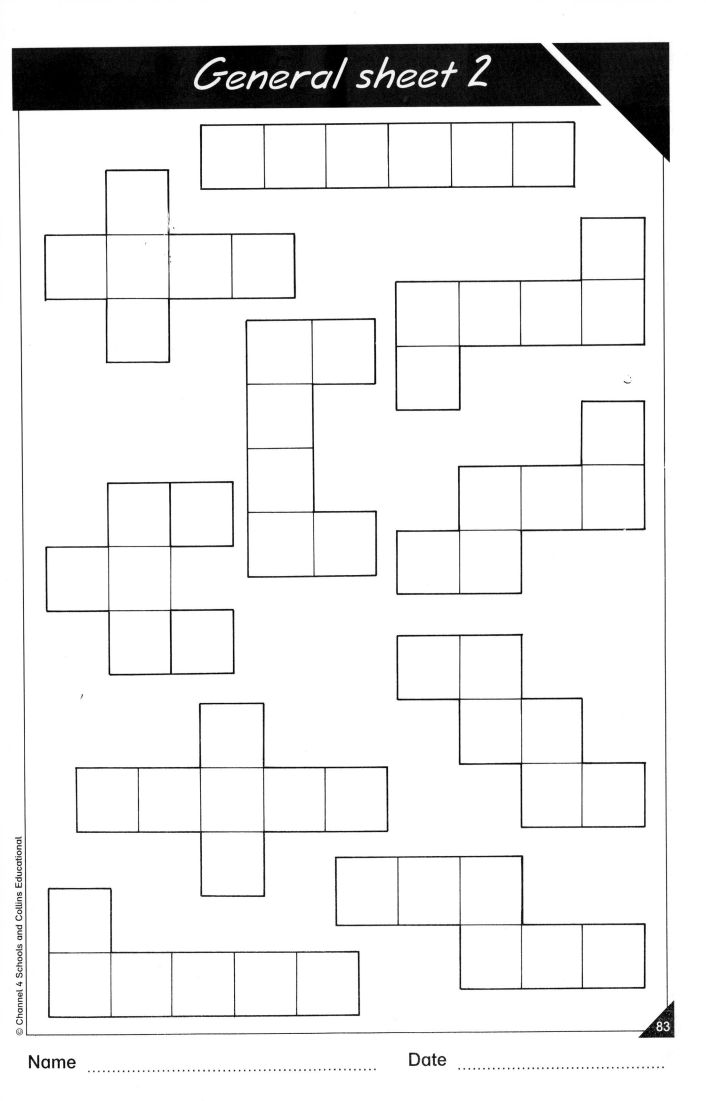

Name .... Date ....

Name .... **Date** ....

Name .... **Date** ....

Sorting Shopping Game Cards

 Dry Cat food 45p

Oranges  15p each

Tea  60p

 Tin of Tomatoes 35p

 Chocolate 55p

£1·45  Tissues

30p each  Grapefruit

Buns £1·30

 Ice Cream £2·30

Bathroom Cleaner  £1·60

Pot-pouri £2·50

Milk 32p

£1·60  Sandwiches

Cat Food  42p

 Toilet paper 82p

Tomatoes 68p per ½ kilo

Biscuits 72p

Name .... **Date** ....

Spaghetti £1·20

Samosas 97p

Cabbage 72p per kilo

Cornflakes £1·19

Washing Powder £2·15

Air Freshner £1·85

Dog Chews 75p

Ball of String £1·30

Jar of Jam 82p

Dog Food £1·05

57p Dog's Ball

Fish Fingers 91p

Candle £1·59

Apple Juice 33p

Guess my card
Pick any card and make up 3 clues so that a friend can guess what is on your card.

Pairs
Place all the cards face down. Take it in turns to turn over any 2 cards. If you can give a good reason why they are in the same set you can keep them. The person with the most pairs at the end is the winner.

Sorting
Sort all your cards into sets. Your friends have to guess how you have sorted them.

My game
Make up your own game and play it with your friends.

Name .... **Date** ....

General sheet 7

1	2	3	4	5	6	7	8	9
10	11	12	13	14	15	16	17	18
19	20	21	22	23	24	25	26	27
28	29	30	31	32	33	34	35	36
37	38	39	40	41	42	43	44	45
46	47	48	49	50	51	52	53	54
55	56	57	58	59	60	61	62	63
64	65	66	67	68	69	70	71	72
73	74	75	76	77	78	79	80	81
82	83	84	85	86	87	88	89	90
91	92	93	94	95	96	97	98	99

1	2	3	4	5	6	7	8	9	10
11	12	13	14	15	16	17	18	19	20
21	22	23	24	25	26	27	28	29	30
31	32	33	34	35	36	37	38	39	40
41	42	43	44	45	46	47	48	49	50
51	52	53	54	55	56	57	58	59	60
61	62	63	64	65	66	67	68	69	70
71	72	73	74	75	76	77	78	79	80
81	82	83	84	85	86	87	88	89	90
91	92	93	94	95	96	97	98	99	100

1	2	3	4	5	6	7
8	9	10	11	12	13	14
15	16	17	18	19	20	21
22	23	24	25	26	27	28
29	30	31	32	33	34	35
36	37	38	39	40	41	42
43	44	45	46	47	48	49
50	51	52	53	54	55	56
57	58	59	60	61	62	63
64	65	66	67	68	69	70
71	72	73	74	75	76	77
78	79	80	81	82	83	84
85	86	87	88	89	90	91
92	93	94	95	96	97	98

1	2	3	4	5	6	7	8
9	10	11	12	13	14	15	16
17	18	19	20	21	22	23	24
25	26	27	28	29	30	31	32
33	34	35	36	37	38	39	40
41	42	43	44	45	46	47	48
49	50	51	52	53	54	55	56
57	58	59	60	61	62	63	64
65	66	67	68	69	70	71	72
73	74	75	76	77	78	79	80
81	82	83	84	85	86	87	88
89	90	91	92	93	94	95	96

Name .... Date ....

Mushrooms	Mushrooms	Mushrooms
Mushrooms	Mushrooms	Mushrooms
Onions	Onions	Onions
Onions	Onions	Onions
Peppers	Peppers	Peppers
Peppers	Peppers	Peppers
Cheese	Cheese	Cheese
Cheese	Cheese	Cheese
Tomatoes	Tomatoes	Tomatoes
Tomatoes	Tomatoes	Tomatoes
Anchovies	Anchovies	Anchovies
Anchovies	Anchovies	Anchovies

Name .... **Date** ....

Name .... **Date** ....

Name .... **Date** ....

Name .... **Date** ....

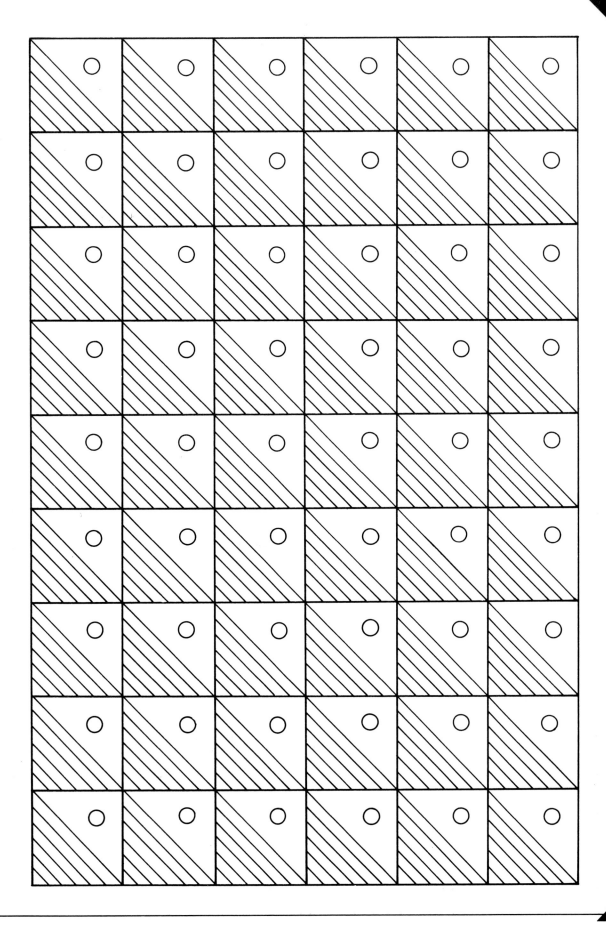

Name .... **Date** ....

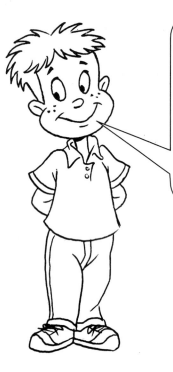

....

....

....

....

....

Pupil record sheet

Name ....

Worksheet	Date	Teacher comment
Shapes of Buildings		
1A Shapes and maps		
1B Sort the buildings		
1C Wall patterns		
1D Skyscrapers		
1E Nets of cubes		
1F Building walls		
Patterns in Buildings		
2A Roof triangles		
2B Making pyramids		
2C Trellis walk		
2D Numbers in triangles		
2E Triangle perimeters		
2F Square numbers		
Inside Shops		
3A Sorting shopping		
3B Design a supermarket		
3C Weighing apples		
3D Stacking apples		
3E Stacking oranges		
3F Best buys		
Living Indoors		
4A Delivering milk		
4B Number 7		
4C Pizzas		
4D Stairs		
4E Pizza fractions		
4F Keeping pets		
Patterns in the Home		
5A Symmetry in the home		
5B Collecting patterns		
5C Rangoli patterns		
5D Rod spiral		
5E Yoruba patterns		
5F Snowflakes		

Did You Know...

there is also a
MATHS EVERYWHERE CD-ROM
available?

This high quality, interactive resource uses real life images to provide an exciting context for mathematical learning. Making full use of graphics, dialogue, music, photographs and video, the challenges are graded to provide motivation for all children in the 7-11 age range.

You can order *Maths Everywhere* CD-Rom, Book 1 and Book 2, plus other Collins Educational books direct from Collins Educational by

Telephone:	0141 306 3484
Fax:	0141 306 3750 or
Post:	Send a photocopy of this completed form to:
	Collins Educational, Harper Collins Publishers,
	FREEPOST GW5078, Bishopbriggs, Glasgow G64 1BR.

Ms/Mrs/Miss/Mr: ....

Position: ....

School: ....

Address: ....

....

.... Postcode: ....

LEA: .... Req No: ....

Please send me, on firm order, the quantity of each title I have stated below:

_____ copies of *Maths Everywhere* **CD-Rom** 0 00 312640 4 @ £79.95 each

_____ copies of *Maths Everywhere* **Book 1** 0 00 312641 2 @ £24.95 each

_____ copies of *Maths Everywhere* **Book 2** 0 00 312642 0 @ £24.95 each

NB: Prices current to December 1995

_____ Please send me further information about Collins Educational resources for Primary Schools

We offer a 10% discount on all orders totalling £150 or more!

Collins Educational